Creation and Science

by
William E. Carroll

Thomas Aquinas Fellow in Theology and Science,
Blackfriars, University of Oxford

*All booklets are published thanks to the
generous support of the members of the
Catholic Truth Society*

CATHOLIC TRUTH SOCIETY
PUBLISHERS TO THE HOLY SEE

Contents

Introduction

After some initial glitches, the Large Hadron Collider began to function as expected in March 2010. Physicists have great hopes that this huge particle accelerator, built underground on the Swiss-French border near Geneva, will provide new and fascinating insights into what the universe was like shortly after the Big Bang. Many in the media have dubbed the accelerator the "Genesis Machine," and it has been easy for some to move to the conclusion that experiments conducted using it will permit us, as one author in *Le Monde* put it, "to make clear the mystery of the creation of the universe."

Almost a decade earlier, the science editor of *The New York Times* predicted that high-speed particle accelerators may help scientists to work out "a mechanistic, gears-and-levers theory of the Genesis moment itself – the hows, if not the whys, of creation *ex nihilo*." Properly speaking, however, these experiments are designed to probe conditions only *after* the Big Bang, not the Big Bang itself.

It seems easy to draw connections between developments in cosmology concerning the beginning of the universe and reflections about creation, but we ought to be alert to what it is that cosmology explains, or seeks to explain, and what creation means. What can cosmologists tell us about the "mystery of the creation of the universe"? An answer to this question requires us to be clear about the explanatory domains of the natural sciences, philosophy, and theology.

Stephen Hawking once famously remarked that his cosmological model, which denied a beginning to the universe, "left nothing for a creator to do." Hawking has expanded his arguments in his recent book, *The Grand Design* (2010), claiming that as a result of recent developments in astrophysics God is not necessary to explain either the precise conditions that existed in the very early universe or the very coming into being of the universe itself. For Hawking, contemporary science has taken over the traditional role of philosophy in addressing ultimate questions about the existence and purpose of the universe. And as he remarked in an interview on television in the United States, "theology is now irrelevant." We will return to Hawking's analyses in the chapter on cosmology and in the conclusion.

Others have embraced traditional Big Bang cosmology, which seems to affirm an absolute beginning to the universe, as providing scientific support for, if not actual confirmation of, the Genesis account of creation. One of the central themes of this book, however, will be that whatever the cosmological model offered, from the Big Bang, to pre-Big Bang scenarios, to multiverse hypotheses, the fundamental understanding of creation remains unaffected. In defending this thesis, we will have to unravel confusions about both creation and the natural sciences.

Such confusion is especially evident in discussions about evolution. As we shall see, there continues to be a widespread belief that one must choose between the conclusions of evolutionary biology and the view that God is the creator of all that is. Chance mutations at the level of genes and the role of natural selection in the origination of new life seem to replace appeals to God as the direct source of new species.

Stuart Kauffman, famous for his work on information systems and bio-complexity, argues that we are "reinventing the sacred" as a result of a new view of science. This new view involves a rejection of reductionism and an affirmation of the emergent properties of a dynamic universe of "ceaseless creativity." As he observes in *Reinventing the Sacred: A New View of Science, Reason, and Religion* (2008):

> life has emerged in the universe without requiring special intervention from a Creator God. . . All, I claim arose without a Creator God. . . Is not this view, a view based on an expanded science, God enough? Is not nature itself creativity enough? What more do we really need of God . . .?

Thus, to accept the dynamism in nature as an explanation of the changes and diversity in and among living things appears to do away with the need for a Creator. Such a view is also behind the fear which informs many believers who reject evolution in order to hold on to the need for a Creator. One must choose, so it seems: either Darwin or God.

We are all too familiar with current debates about creation and evolution. Despite the extreme views of "young Earth creationists," what is at issue in these debates is not some naïve view that the Earth is only 10,000 years old. Rather, for many believers, however old the world is, God is necessary to explain the order and design evident in it. At times this view has come to mean that God has directly intervened to create each of the different species of living things. It is precisely such an understanding of creation that many people think evolution denies. Not only does natural selection replace divine agency, but chance supplants order and design in explanations of the origin of life. As the American philosopher Daniel Dennett remarks: "Science has won and religion has lost. Darwin's idea has banished the Book of Genesis to the limbo of quaint mythology."

The sense of a fundamental incompatibility between creation and evolution is part of a wider intellectual framework in which scientific developments have been used to support a kind of "totalizing naturalism." This is the view that the universe and the processes within it need no explanation beyond the categories of the natural sciences. We will explore this broader topic, namely, that the natural sciences, in particular biology and cosmology, have shown us that we do not need a Creator. The argument is that contemporary science is fully sufficient, at least in principle, to account for all that needs to be accounted for in the universe.

Whether we speak of explanations of the Big Bang itself (such as quantum tunneling from nothing) or of some version of a multiverse hypothesis, or of self-organizing principles in biological change (including, at times, appeals to randomness and chance as ultimate explanations), the conclusion which seems inescapable to many is that there is no need to appeal to a creator, that is, to any cause which is outside the natural order. Indeed, writing at the beginning of the Twentieth Century, a German chemist, Heinrich Caro, noted that "science has conducted God to its frontiers, thanking him for his provisional services."

In later chapters we will return to developments in contemporary cosmology and evolutionary biology and examine the ways in which many draw conclusions about creation based on these developments. In the intermediate chapters we will look at what "to create" means, both in a theological and in a philosophical sense, so that we can return to the contemporary debate better informed and better able to dispel much of the confusion. As the reader will discover, I think that the understanding of creation, and the relationship between creation and the natural sciences, forged by St Thomas Aquinas (1224-1274) has continuing relevance for us today.

This book is not so much a source of information about specific developments in contemporary science as it is an examination of the ways in which these developments are used to comment upon creation. The analysis concerns ideas not practices. Throughout, the word "creation" means the act by which God causes things to exist, as distinct from the results of such action. "Science" in this context refers to knowledge of nature or claims about such knowledge and not to related topics in technology or bioethics.

Discussions of creation and its relationship to the natural sciences are not unique to Christianity. Muslim and Jewish scholars have long reflected on this topic. In fact, in the Middle Ages, Maimonides (1135-1204), the great Jewish philosopher and theologian, observed that a commitment to the doctrine of creation was shared by Judaism, Islam, and Christianity. Maimonides was not sure, given Christianity's doctrine of the Trinity, whether Christians could be correctly called monotheists. He did think that all three religious traditions recognized the absolute sovereignty of God who is the cause of existence. Christian thinkers, especially Thomas Aquinas, were influenced by Muslim and Jewish analyses of creation; nevertheless, in this book, the focus will be on the Christian doctrine of creation. The topic is vast and the presentation here is necessarily selective, reflecting the interests and emphases of the author. Furthermore, the reader should remember that this book only offers a broad introduction to a wide array of related issues. More detailed analyses would require a much longer text. My hope is that this book will whet one's intellectual appetite for further study.

Although I have referred to texts by various authors, I have refrained from using many footnotes, in keeping with the general approach of books in this series. At the end of this book I have listed a few references for further reading.

Genesis and the Origins of Creation

When believers and non-believers discuss the relationship between the Christian understanding of creation and the claims of science, they often appeal to the stories in the Book of Genesis as the definitive account of what creation entails. The two stories of creation contained in the initial book of the Bible have been the subject of extensive commentary and analysis for centuries. If one were to read the opening of the Book of Genesis without any reference to the history of Christian thought, it would not be immediately obvious that the first words, "In the beginning God created the heavens and the earth," are an affirmation of creation out of nothing.

In fact, there continues to be considerable disagreement as to what the opening words of the Bible are. A representative contemporary English translation, found in the New English Bible, reads:

> In the beginning of creation, when God made heaven and earth, the earth was without form and void, with darkness over the face of the abyss, and a mighty wind that swept over the surface of the waters.

Such a rendering of the original Hebrew text would certainly seem to call into question an explicit source in

Genesis of the doctrine of creation out of nothing. Furthermore, scholars do not agree on how properly to translate the word *bara*, the word which becomes *creavit* in the Latin translation. It is not clear, from a purely linguistic point of view, that the Hebrew verb *necessarily* means to create out of nothing.

The opening of Genesis is not the earliest text in the Bible. It received its final written form only during the period of the Babylonian exile of the Jewish people. The prophets of Israel remind the Jews, in the midst of their pessimism, that their God is not like other gods. God who has made a covenant with Abraham and who brought His people out of Egypt is the Creator of all that is. Hebrew scriptures return, from time to time, to this theme. Indeed, immediately following the initial account of creation in Genesis there is a second story of origins, a story composed before the first and containing different imagery. Throughout the Bible there are various images and modes of speaking which bear witness to the fundamental truth of God's creative act. We can find such commentary in the Psalms, in the Wisdom literature, and in the Second Book of Maccabees. Most biblical scholarship today would deny that we can find in the Bible any clearly unambiguous commitment which excludes God's using pre-existent matter in what Scripture refers to as creation.

How does one Read the Bible?

The question of reading the opening line of Genesis –
aside from identifying what that line is – is part of a
much larger question: how does one read the Bible?
When we look at the development of the Christian
doctrine of creation we must remember how Christians
in the early Church and in the Middle Ages – when that
doctrine was formed – approached the evidence from
biblical revelation. They read Genesis, for example, not
as an isolated account of origins, but as part of a whole,
which could be understood only with Christ in mind.
Thus, for example, Christians read the opening of
Genesis in the light of the opening of the Gospel of John,
thus identifying "in the beginning" with "in/through
Christ." Creation and salvation were intimately linked:
Christ is the origin and end of all things.

The more recent concern for the biblical text as a
historical document, connected to the times and culture
in which it was composed, often excludes the
consideration of how each text is an integral part of the
Bible as a whole. Such an approach to the Bible leads
many to question whether the opening line of Genesis
can really support the doctrine of creation out of nothing.

The Bible is not a theological textbook; it does not
contain a series of isolated theological propositions.
Christian doctrines find their origin in biblical revelation,

but they are formulated as the Christian community reflects on the content of what is believed. It was, for example, only as the early Church reflected on who Christ was and what He had done that doctrinal statements were developed to capture the understanding of what was believed. The early councils of the Church, such as Nicaea (325 AD) and Chalcedon (451 AD), gave clear expression to what it meant for Christ to be both fully divine and fully human. As we shall see, it is the Fourth Lateran Council of 1215 which provides the first doctrinal definition of creation.

There is an important distinction that needs to be kept in mind when we discuss the relationship between creation and the natural sciences, especially when discussing the biblical account of creation. There is a difference between God's causing all that is to be and the account of the "six days of creation" set forth in Genesis. Often we find in the hexaemeral literature of Patristic and mediaeval authors elaborate attempts to discover a concordance between the description of the formation of the world and what was the best scientific knowledge of the day. The ways in which various features of the universe are formed, and the putative order of their formation, is a separate topic from the recognition that, however things came to develop, God is the absolute origin of whatever is.

Augustine on Science and Scripture

Even today, it seems to many that the opening of the Book of Genesis, unlike the other parts of the Bible, addresses scientific questions; that, here at least, the Bible and science overlap and that, accordingly a believer must take into account what the Bible says when discussing the origin and development of the universe even when the specific subject has nothing to do with salvation. I have already noted that throughout the history of the Church there have been attempts to find correlations between the "six days" described in Genesis and scientific knowledge. Thus, there appears to be a special problem for anyone who tries to find, for example, a concordance between evolution and what Genesis describes – or who rejects one in defense of the other.

Long ago, however, St Augustine (354-430) recognized that the Bible was not written to offer scientific accounts of nature. He knew that through sense experience and rational reflection human beings could come to know many things about the world in which they lived. When scholars do come to such knowledge, it should be respected. Augustine thought that the Bible ought never to be interpreted in such a way that scientific truths about nature are contradicted by appeals to Scripture. The Bible is not written to instruct human beings about this world: it is written to offer knowledge about the next world, and about man's behavior and man's relation to God. The Bible does mention natural phenomena, but the purpose of doing so is not to teach us about these phenomena: the purpose of the Bible is religious and moral, not scientific.

Augustine saw two great dangers in treating the Bible as though it were a scientific text and of interpreting it in such a way that it appeared to be at variance with the conclusions of science. First, interpreting the Bible in such a way opens it up to the ridicule of non-believers. If non-believers know something about nature and find that what they know is contradicted by Scripture, what reason will they have for believing the Bible on other matters (for example, eternal life) that properly belong to Christian faith? Second, those who are weak in the faith can have their faith destroyed if they find that scientists hold views about nature contrary to what is supposed to be in the Bible.

Underpinning Augustine's position is the fundamental Christian teaching, which was given clear formulation by Thomas Aquinas, that the truths of the Christian religion can never be contradicted by the truths of the natural sciences, and vice versa. This is so because the very same God who revealed the truths of faith also created the universe in which the truths of science have their foundation. He created human beings with their capacity to come to know what the world was like. Truth cannot contradict truth! If there is ever the appearance of a contradiction between Christian faith and science, such an appearance is an indication of either an inadequate understanding of faith or a mistaken conception of science, or both.

Doctrinal Pronouncements on Creation

Direct appeals to the Bible, with little if any reference to the history and development of Christian doctrine - appeals which treat the Bible in a kind of splendid (if unwarranted) isolation from the long tradition of its interpretation - would not offer an adequate sense of what it means to say that God creates all that is. Nevertheless, the Church's teaching on creation is clear.

The Christian doctrine of creation is made explicit in the decrees of both the Fourth Lateran Council (1215) and the First Vatican Council (1870), and these texts provide the normative statement of what it means to say that God is the Creator. Thus, any discussion of creation and science ought to begin with the clear understanding of creation set forth in these two councils.

In response to the dangers of the Albigensian heresy which denied that God alone is the cause of all that is, both material and spiritual things, the Fourth Lateran Council issued what was the first magisterial definition of creation:

We firmly believe and simply confess that there is only one true God. . . one principle of all things [*unum universorum principium*], creator of all things visible and invisible, spiritual and corporeal; who by his almighty power altogether at the beginning of time [*simul ab initio temporis*] created from nothing [*de nihilo condidit*] both spiritual and corporeal creatures, that is to say angelic and earthly. . .

At the First Vatican Council, the Church, in reaffirming the decree of the Fourth Lateran Council, was also especially concerned to reject various forms of materialism as well as any position which denied the complete dependence of all that is on God. The dogmatic definition and associated canons of condemnation represent the fullest magisterial statement concerning creation.

The Holy, Catholic, Apostolic, and Roman Church believes and confesses that there is one true and living God, creator and lord of heaven and earth, almighty, eternal, immeasurable, incomprehensible, infinite in will, understanding and every perfection. Since he is one, singular, completely simple and unchangeable spiritual substance, he must be declared to be in reality and in essence, distinct from the world, supremely happy in himself and from himself, and inexpressibily loftier than anything besides himself which either exists or can be imagined. This one true God, by his goodness and almighty power, not with the intention of increasing his happiness, nor indeed of attaining happiness, but in order to manifest his perfection by the good things which he bestows on what he creates, by an absolutely free plan, together from the beginning of time brought into being from nothing the twofold created order, that is the spiritual and the corporeal, the angelic and the earthly . . .

We shall have occasion to return to features of the dogmatic definition of creation as we look at the ways in which theologians, especially Thomas Aquinas, came to understand it, but it is worth noting here the emphases on creation's being "out of nothing" and that there is a temporal beginning to the created order, that is, that the universe is not eternal.

Furthermore, we should note the affirmation that God's creative act is free and that God is not better off, as it were, because God creates. Creation is a manifestation of God's goodness. To make it clear that there is a radical difference between Creator and creatures, canons of the First Vatican Council warn against any attempt to view God and the world as being of the same substance [that is, any kind of pantheism] or that creatures are somehow the result of a bubbling over [a certain kind of necessary emanation] from the divine being. Note that the doctrinal definition of creation says nothing about the six days described in Genesis; it simply affirms the fact that God is the cause of all that is.

Although the origins of the Christian understanding of creation are prior to theological and philosophical reflections, it is in the encounter between philosophy and science, on the one hand, and the insights derived from Scripture, on the other, that the *doctrine* of creation is forged and then made explicit in conciliar decrees. We need to remember that doctrines, even Church doctrines, have their origins in time, place, and historical circumstance. Such rootedness in history does not invalidate claims for a truth of doctrine transcending time and place, but it does mean that as we seek to understand the doctrine – a task which is both philosophical and theological – we need the assistance of history.

Faith, Reason, and Creation

A brief examination of the historical discussion of creation can help make clear what creation means and illuminate as well contemporary discussions, since many of the issues raised today about creation and science were the subject of sustained reflection in earlier times – even if we recognize significant differences in what the natural sciences tell us about the world.

Church Fathers, Greek Philosophy, and Creation

When theologians in the second, third, and fourth centuries came to define the Christian view of nature, human nature, and God – as distinct from the views found in the pagan intellectual world in which they lived – they found in Genesis, interpreted in the light of Christian faith, a source for a view of God as creator which they developed into an understanding of the origin of the universe characteristically their own.

The Hellenistic world in which the early Christian theologians sought to understand their faith shared an intellectual patrimony which, despite its diversity, maintained that the universe is eternal. From Heraclitus and Parmenides to Plato and Aristotle, and from the Stoics to Plotinus, the ancient philosophers appeared to speak with one voice. Whether there be nothing but change or change be an illusion, whether we distinguish between a world of becoming and a world of being, or between potentiality and actuality, one thing is clear: there is no absolute temporal beginning of the universe.

For the Church Fathers, Christian revelation stood out in stark contrast to this traditional view of an eternal universe. For early Christians to say that the world is eternal is to make it equal to God. God alone is eternal; the world is finite, and this includes temporal finitude; the world began to be. Furthermore an eternal universe appeared to be a necessary universe, a universe which was not the result of the free act of a transcendent God.

Also for the Church Fathers, the view that the world is eternal, in the specific sense of being without a finite temporal duration, seemed inevitably to require a cyclical view of history, a view that would raise fundamental problems for Christianity. Only a temporally finite world could constitute the scene for the religious drama of Fall and Redemption, with its central, unique, unrepeatable event: the coming of Christ. Only in a world temporally finite did it seem possible to make sense of the Christian understanding of each person's destiny providentially designed by a loving God. If salvation history is to make sense, time cannot be cyclical.

Crucial as well was the recognition that creation is out of nothing. There is no pre-existent material which God uses in the act of creating. Creation is not a transforming of formless material into the structure of the world; creation is the complete and total production of all that is. Any kind of cosmological dualism must be rejected. All that is has God as its source. If everything that is depends upon God for its very existence, creation must be out of nothing. If there were some pre-existent material with which God worked, that material would not depend upon God for its existence.

A world that has an absolute beginning in time and which is created out of nothing seemed incomprehensible to both philosophy and science. After all, ancient scholars thought it was surely the case that the world is eternal and that it was impossible to get something from nothing. Not even an all-powerful being can accomplish what is in principle impossible. Must one reject science (and, in the process, reason) in order to accept a central truth of Christianity? How Christian thinkers wrestled with such a question offers important insights for debates about creation and science in our day.

Thomas Aquinas on Creation

Mediaeval discussions about creation (especially the intelligibility of *creatio ex nihilo*), divine agency, and the autonomy of nature, and ultimately the very possibility of the natural sciences' discovering real causes in nature, provide a rich source of insights for us today. These discussions occurred in the religious communities of Islam, Judaism, and Christianity. What Avicenna, Maimonides, and Thomas Aquinas, for example, saw so clearly, that creation is an account of the existence of things, not of changes in and among things, allows us to conclude that there is no contradiction between creation, so understood, and any conclusion in the natural sciences. The natural sciences have as their domain of explanation the world of changing things. Whether the changes so described are biological or cosmological, without beginning or end, or temporally finite, they remain processes. We will return to this theme in the next chapters when we look at features of the contemporary debate about creation and science.

The key to Thomas Aquinas' analysis is the distinction he draws between creation and change, or, as he often remarked: *creatio non est mutatio* (creation is not a change). Creation, as a metaphysical and theological notion, affirms that all that is, in whatever way or ways it is, depends upon God as cause. The natural sciences, whether Aristotelian (with which Thomas was primarily concerned) or those of our own day, have as their subject the world of changing things: from subatomic particles to acorns to galaxies. Whenever there is a change there must be something that changes.

Creation, on the other hand, is the radical causing of the whole existence of whatever exists. To cause completely something to exist is not to produce a change in something, is not to work on or with some existing material. If, in producing something new, an agent were to use something already existing, the agent would not be the *complete* cause of the new thing. But such complete causing is precisely what creation is. To create is to cause existence, and all things are totally dependent upon the Creator for the very fact that they are. As Thomas remarks in his treatise, *On Separated Substances* [chapter 9]: "Over and above the mode of becoming by which something comes to be through change or motion, there must be a mode of becoming or origin of things without any mutation or motion, through the influx of being."

Modern arguments about order and design (like mediaeval arguments about motion and an unmoved mover) are arguments in natural philosophy and not in metaphysics. To the extent that "to create" is susceptible to rational examination, it is a topic in metaphysics and not in natural philosophy, nor in the individual empirical sciences.

Creatures are what they are (including those which are free), precisely because God is present to them as cause. Were God to withdraw, all that exists would cease to be. Creaturely agency and the integrity of nature, in general, are guaranteed by God's creative causality.

Furthermore, for Thomas, creation is not primarily some distant event; rather, it is the on-going complete causing of the existence of all that is. At this very moment, were God not causing all that is to exist – from subatomic particles to the color of the sky, to our own thoughts, hopes, and dreams – were God not to be causing everything that is, there would be nothing at all.

Human creations and Creation

To avoid confusion, we need to recognize the different senses of how we use the term "to create." We often speak of human creations, especially with respect to the production of works of art, music, and literature. What it means for God to create is radically different from any kind of human making. When human beings make things they work with already existing material to produce something new. The human act of creating is not the complete cause of what is produced; but God's creative act is the complete cause of what is produced; this sense of being the complete cause is captured in the expression "out of nothing." To be such a complete cause of all that is requires an infinite power, and no creature, no human being, possesses such infinite power. God wills things to be and thus they are. To say that God is the complete cause of all that is does not negate the role of other causes which are part of the created natural order. Creatures, both animate and inanimate, are real causes of the wide array of changes that occur in the world, but God alone is the universal cause of being as such. God's causality is so different from the causality of creatures that there is no competition between the two, that is, we do not need to limit, as it were, God's causality to make room for the causality of creatures. God causes creatures to be causes.

Creation as an Origin, Not a Beginning

Thomas Aquinas is particularly insightful in distinguishing between the origin of the universe and the beginning of the universe. Beginning refers to a temporal event, and an absolute beginning of the universe would be an event which is coincident with the beginning of time. Creation is an account of the origin, or source of existence, of the universe, and, as such, Thomas thinks that creation can be demonstrated in the discipline of metaphysics.

For Thomas there are two senses of creation out of nothing, one philosophical, the other theological. The philosophical sense means that God, with no material cause, makes all things to exist as entities that are really different from Him, yet completely dependent upon His causality. The theological sense of creation denies nothing of the philosophical sense but adds to it, among other things, the notion that the created universe is temporally finite. The Creator is prior to what is created, but the priority is not *fundamentally* temporal. Each creature has its origin in the Creator and is wholly dependent upon the Creator for its existence; the dependence is metaphysical not temporal. To be created out of nothing does not mean that the creature is *first* nothing and *then* something.

Thomas saw no contradiction in the notion of an eternal created universe. For, even if the universe had no temporal beginning, it still would depend upon God for its very being. The radical dependence on God as cause of being is what creation means. Thomas, of course, accepted as a matter of faith that the Bible revealed that the world had an absolute temporal beginning, which obviously meant that it had to be created, but he thought that reason alone (in philosophy or science) could not know whether the universe had a temporal beginning or whether it was eternal. He did think, however, that reason alone (in metaphysics), by reflecting on what it means for things to exist, could conclude for sure that there must be an Uncaused Cause of all that is.[1]

Theology of Creation and Science

When it came to explaining the opening verses of Genesis, especially the events described in the "six days of creation," Thomas observed that what was central to Christian faith was the "fact of creation" and not the "manner or mode" of formation of the world. Questions concerning order, design, and chance in nature refer to the "manner or mode" of formation of the world. Attempts in the natural sciences to explain these facets of nature do not challenge the "fact of creation." A world with a temporal beginning concerns the kind of world God has created. It may very well be easier to accept that a world which has an absolute temporal beginning is a created world, and such a world may be especially appropriate for understanding sacred history, important as it is for believers. But an eternal world, one without a beginning to time, would be no less a created world.

Creation understood theologically completes and perfects what philosophy discloses about God as cause of the existence of all that is. With respect to the relationship between creation and science, the subject of this book, the insights of faith concerning the Trinitarian nature of God as Creator, with the dynamic inner life of the three Divine Persons being freely expressed externally in the creation of all that is, connected to the drama of the Fall and Redemption, and seeing "in the beginning" to mean in/through Christ, are not particularly relevant. That theological feature of creation which is relevant is the temporal beginning of the world. But even this concerns more the kind of universe God creates than it does the core sense of creation, which is ontological dependence. Accordingly, throughout the discussion of creation and science, it will be the philosophical sense of creation – a sense which is indeed included in the Christian theology of creation – which will occupy our attention.

Cosmology and Creation

With an understanding of the traditional sense of creation out-of-nothing, especially as set forth by Thomas Aquinas, we are better prepared to return to some of the themes noted in the "Introduction" and thus to examine contemporary challenges to the doctrine of creation, based on appeals to science.

Fascination with origins is common-place in the natural sciences. The cover of the September 2009 issue of *Scientific American* announced the theme for a wide variety of essays on "Understanding Origins." Topics included: the origins of teeth, of cooking, of chocolate, of paper money, of the internal combustion engine, and of intermittent windshield wipers. Most prominently displayed on the cover, however, were origins of life and of the universe. Michael Turner of the University of Chicago was the author of the essay on the origin of the universe and he optimistically claimed that "cosmologists are closing in on the ultimate processes that created and shaped the universe." Turner drew a compelling picture of the many advances in cosmology over the last one hundred years which have radically transformed our understanding of the universe and its development, from a kind of "formless soup of elementary particles" into "the richly structured cosmos of today."

The 'Limitless Power of Science'

Developments in cosmology and particle physics have long encouraged flights of fancy about what the natural sciences can discover about the world. Perhaps one of the more extravagant claims about what contemporary science can tell us about the origin and nature of the universe can be found in an essay, "The Limitless Power of Science," written by the Oxford physical chemist, Peter Atkins, several years ago. Atkins claimed that the domain of scientific discourse is truly limitless; there is no corner of the universe, no dimension of reality, no feature of human existence, which is not properly the subject of the modern natural sciences! Atkins has little use for philosophy as a guide to truth, but it is religion which is the special object of his ire; theology, he thinks, has contributed nothing to our understanding of reality. On the other hand:

> Scientists liberate truth from prejudice, and through their work lend wings to society's aspirations. While poetry titillates and theology obfuscates, science liberates. The grave responsibility of scientists is to use their voices to blow back the fog that shrouds the minds of those who have not yet seen.

The science embraced by Atkins truly knows no limits. Creation itself falls within its grasp. Science, he writes, must be able to account for the "emergence of everything from absolutely nothing. Not almost nothing, not a subatomic dust-like speck, but absolutely nothing. Nothing at all. Not even empty space." Following in Atkins' footsteps, Christopher Hitchens in his popular book, *God is Not Great* contends: "Religion has run out of justifications. Thanks to the telescope and the microscope, it no longer offers an explanation of anything important." In fact, as the sub-title of his book urges, he thinks religion "poisons everything." It is a view widely shared in the circles of the "new atheism."

'Nothing for a Creator to do'

Even if we were to reject the overly exuberant rhetoric of Atkins and Hitchens, it seems easy to draw connections between developments in cosmology concerning the beginning of the universe and theological reflections about creation. Nevertheless, we ought to be alert to what it is that cosmology explains, or seeks to explain, and what creation means. Stephen Hawking once famously remarked that his cosmological model, which denied a beginning to the universe, "left nothing for a creator to do." Here are Hawking's now famous words:

> So long as the universe had a beginning, we could suppose it had a creator. But if the universe is really completely self-contained, having no boundary or edge, it would have neither beginning nor end: it would simply be. What place, then, for a creator?

New theories concerning what happened "before the Big Bang" as well as those which speak of an endless series of big bangs are often attractive because they too deny a fundamental beginning to the universe and thus appear to make a Creator irrelevant.

Recently, there has been considerable fascination with various multiverse hypotheses, according to which our universe is but one of a very large number – or perhaps an infinite number – of universes. If our universe is but one of an infinite number, it just happens to be and does not need an explanation for its particular characteristics. Multiverse proposals are often advanced to avoid what for many are unpleasant consequences of arguments about the "fine-tuning" of the initial conditions of our universe: fine-tuning which many think would be evidence for God as fine-tuner. But fine-tuning is not creation; furthermore, however many "universes" there may be, even an infinite number, they would all depend upon God's creative act in order to be.

The Big Bang as Evidence for Creation

There are other scholars who have embraced traditional Big Bang cosmology, which seems to affirm an absolute beginning to the universe, as providing scientific support for, if not actual confirmation of, the Genesis account of creation. The argument is that an initial "singularity" such as the Big Bang, outside the categories of space and time, points to a supernatural cause of the beginning of the universe. If one can say that, in fact, the universe began to exist, then, so the argument goes, there must be a cause of this fact, and this cause must obviously be external to the universe; hence there must be a Creator. In a way, the debate is about whether or not cosmology discloses a beginning of the universe and thus whether cosmology rejects or embraces the idea of creation. Despite fundamental differences as to what contemporary cosmology tells us about the beginning of the universe (from those theories which deny there is a beginning to those which accept the "singularity" as such a beginning), all these views tend to identify what it means for the universe to be created with its having a temporal beginning. They equate to be created with to have a beginning; they miss the fundamental point that creation concerns origins not beginnings.

Creation and the 'First Principle of Cosmology'

There is a broader methodological issue at play here: what precisely is the competence of the natural sciences when it comes to discussions about the origin of the universe? One cosmologist, Lee Smolin, in *Three Roads to Quantum Gravity* (2001), raises this topic and offers a succinct account of the self-sufficient universe which he thinks must be embraced by scientists:

We humans are the species that makes things. So when we find something that appears to be beautifully and intricately structured, our almost instinctive response is to ask, 'Who made that?' The most important lesson to be learned if we are to prepare ourselves to approach the universe scientifically is that this is not the right question to ask. It is true that the universe is as beautiful as it is intrinsically structured. But it cannot have been made by anything that exists outside of it, for by definition the universe is all there is, and there can be nothing outside it. And, by definition, neither can there have been anything before the universe that caused it, for if anything existed it must have been part of the universe. So the first principle of cosmology must be 'There is nothing outside the universe.'. . . The first principle means that we take the universe to be, by definition, a closed system. It means that the explanation for anything in the universe can involve only other things that also exist in the universe.

Thus, whatever kind of "creation" science can disclose, or be used to deny, through particle accelerators or elaborate mathematical models, it would be a scientific account of origins employing, as Smolin would say, principles drawn from within the universe. But such a conception of "creation" is not what philosophers and theologians mean when they speak of creation.

The Big Bang is Not Creation

The distance between minute fractions of a second after the Big Bang and creation is, in a sense, infinite. We do not get closer to creation by getting closer to the Big Bang. Since creation is not really an event at all, it is not within the explanatory domain of cosmology; it is a subject for metaphysics and theology. Some cosmologists have used insights from quantum mechanics to offer accounts of the Big Bang itself. They speak of the Big Bang in terms of "quantum tunnelling from nothing," analogous to the way in which very small particles seem to emerge from vacuums in laboratory experiments. Thus, they think that to explain the Big Bang in this way eliminates the need to have a Creator.

But the Big Bang "explained" in this way is still a change and, as we have seen, creation, properly understood is not a change at all. Similarly, the "nothing" in these cosmological models which speak of "quantum tunnelling from nothing" is not the nothing referred to in the traditional sense of creation out of nothing. The "nothing" in cosmological reflections may very well be nothing like our present universe, but it is not the absolute nothing central to what it means to create; it is only that about which the theories say nothing. The crucial point here is that to offer a scientific account of the Big Bang is not to say anything about whether or not the universe is created.

Confusions concerning creation and cosmology, as I have suggested, run the gamut from denials of creation because the universe is conceived as having no beginning, to explanations of a beginning in exclusively scientific terms which avoid any appeal to a Creator, to an endless series of universes within universes, or to opposing claims that the Big Bang itself offers a kind of scientific warrant for belief in God's creation of the universe.

Creation as a Concept in Metaphysics and Theology, not in Cosmology

Contrary to all these claims about implications of cosmological theories for creation, we need to recognize that creation is a metaphysical and theological affirmation that all that is depends upon God as cause. The natural sciences have as their subject the world of changing things. Whenever there is a change there must be something that changes. Whether these changes are biological or cosmological, without beginning or end, or temporally finite, they remain processes.

Creation, on the other hand, is the radical causing of the whole existence of whatever exists. Creation is not a change. To cause completely something to exist is not to produce a change in something, is not to work on or with some existing material. When God's creative act is said to be "out of nothing," what is meant is that God does not use anything in creating all that is: it does not mean that there is a change from "nothing" to "something." Cosmology and all the other natural sciences offer accounts of change; they do not address the metaphysical and theological questions of creation; they do not speak of why there is something rather than nothing. It is a mistake to use arguments in the natural sciences to deny creation. It is also a mistake to appeal to cosmology as a confirmation of creation. Reason (as well as faith) can lead to knowledge of the Creator, but the path is in metaphysics not in the natural sciences. Discussions of creation are different from arguments from order and design to a source of order and design. Creation offers an explanation of why things exist at all.

As we have seen, Thomas Aquinas thought that neither science nor philosophy could know whether the universe had a beginning. He did think that metaphysics could show us that the universe is created, but he would have warned against those today who use Big Bang cosmology, for example, to conclude that the universe has a beginning and therefore must be created. He was always alert to reject the use of bad arguments in support of what is believed.

The "singularity" in traditional Big Bang cosmology may represent the beginning of the universe we observe, but we cannot conclude that it is the absolute beginning, the kind of beginning which would indicate creation. As some contemporary cosmologists recognize, there could very well be something before the Big Bang. Indeed, Gabriele Veneziano, a theoretical physicist at CERN and one of the fathers of string theory in the late 1960s, observes that "the pre-bang universe has become the latest frontier of cosmology." The title of his essay in The *Scientific American* (2004) is instructive: "The Myth of the Beginning of Time."

But, since reason remains silent about an absolute beginning, all theories about a universe without such a beginning remain speculations. Thus, in the midst of such theories about an eternal universe or some kind of multiverse, were faith to insist on a beginning there is no conflict between faith and science. Speculations about a universe without a beginning are not the same as scientific truth about the universe. Remember, as well, that the core sense of creation refers to a dependency upon God, not the beginning of time.

Evolution and Creation

Discussions about creation and evolution can easily become obscured in broader political, social, and philosophical contexts. Indeed, evolution and creation have taken on cultural connotations, serve as ideological markers, with the result that each has come to stand for a competing world-view. For some, to embrace evolution is to affirm an exclusively secular and atheistic view of reality, and evolution is accordingly either welcomed or rejected on such grounds.

Writing in *The Evolution-Creation Struggle* (2005), Michael Ruse argues that "creationism" and what he calls "evolutionism" represent rival religious views of the world: "rival stories of origins, rival judgments about the meaning of human life, rival sets of moral dictates. . . ." What Ruse calls "evolutionism" is a collection of cultural claims which have their roots in, but ought to be distinguished from, the scientific discipline of evolutionary biology. Similarly, too often "creation" is confused with various forms of "creationism," which embrace either a literalistic reading of the Bible or think that creation *must* mean a kind of divine intervention in cosmic history with God's directly creating each individual species of living things.

The choice for many seems to be between a purely natural explanation of the origin and development of life, an explanation in terms of common descent, genetic mutations, and natural selection as the mechanism of biological change, on the one hand, and, on the other hand, an explanation which sees divine agency as the source of life in all its diversity and that human beings, created in the image and likeness of God, have a special place in the universe. The difference *appears* stark: either Darwin or God.

One source of confusion in such an analysis is to see God's creative act essentially as the explanation for order and design in nature: that is, to identify creation with the causing of order and design. As evolutionary biology, for example, claims to be able to explain order and design without an appeal to an orderer or designer, but exclusively on the basis of natural processes, it appears to many that there is no longer a role for God to play. It is an error, however, to think that an explanation of order is an explanation of existence, and creation refers to God as cause of existence.

Self-organization in Living Things

In contemporary biology, there have been important discussions about understanding living things in terms of "self-organization." As we saw in the "Introduction," Stuart Kauffman writes of the "ceaseless creativity" in nature and that, accordingly, we ought to conclude that nature itself is creativity enough; there is no need for a Creator. As reductionism and mechanism are being replaced by appeals to dynamic, intrinsic, organizing principles, the conclusion often reached is that changes in nature are exhaustively based on principles and entities in the natural world, and that there is no need for any external "interference" to explain the change. Terrence Deacon, author of *The Symbolic Species: The Co-evolution of Language and the Brain* (1997), makes the following claim: "Evolution is the one kind of process able to produce something out of nothing. . . [A]n evolutionary process is an origination process . . . Evolution is the author of its spontaneous creations."

Previously, in a Newtonian universe, when nature was conceived in exclusively inert and mechanistic terms, there were appeals to a source of activity beyond nature, although such appeals would often never be more than the affirmation of a kind of deism: to see God as only getting things started, so to speak; although there may be times when he has to tinker with the mechanism he has produced. But as Thomas Aquinas has shown us, creation is not essentially some distant event, it is the on-going, complete causing of all that is. The God of deism is not the Creator affirmed by Christianity. Furthermore, as I have already indicated, for many thinkers today there is no category beyond change and the specific behavior of individual things that requires an explanation. It is important to distinguish between the particular claims which evolutionary biology makes about the development and diversity of living things, explanations which are properly in the domain of the natural sciences, and philosophical claims concerning whether or not additional explanations of these realities are necessary. An important point here is that to defend the competence of the natural sciences to describe what happens in nature ought not to be equated with a denial of creation.

The extent to which biologists, when they speak about self-organization, move beyond the domain of biology to make broad claims about "self-creation" and that, accordingly, there is no need to appeal to a source of existence of living things, is the extent to which their claims are broadly metaphysical. An important feature of these philosophical claims, namely, that "self-creation" and "self-sufficiency" evident in the natural order eliminate the need to appeal to God, involves conceptions of God and creation which, even if shared by some believers, are really not the same as those found in traditional philosophy and theology. Remember that all the natural sciences explain change in and among existing things, and creation is not a change.

The 'Divine Foot' and the Methodology of Naturalism

Much like Lee Smolin in his arguments concerning cosmology, the Harvard biologist, Richard Lewontin, has warned that science must guard against allowing a "Divine Foot into the door" of explanations of nature. All truly scientific explanations, he argues, must be framed in terms of what is often called the methodology of naturalism - a methodology which must be rigorously protected and which, for many, involves a commitment to a metaphysical naturalism which is a modern form of materialism.

The fear of the "Divine Foot" is based on a philosophical understanding (and ultimately, I would argue, misunderstanding) of the Creator and of divine agency. For Lewontin, God would be a competing cause in the world. The fear is that any causality one attributes to God must, accordingly, be denied to creatures. This is precisely the fear which informs many who defend creation against evolution as well as those who defend evolution against creation: both opposing sides view the general terms of the discourse in the same way. In either case, God and creatures are seen (erroneously) to be causes which, although differing significantly in degree, fall within the same explanatory category. Accordingly, the more one appeals to nature as self-explanatory, the less one appeals to God – or vice versa.

God as Cause and Creatures as Causes

The problem which those who defend a self-sufficiency in nature and its processes see is that any appeal to a cause outside of nature is either superfluous or contradictory to the very claim that nature is the domain of self-organizing activities. There is a confusion here, however, about different orders or levels of explanation.

If we ask, for example, why wood is heated in the presence of fire, we can explain the phenomenon in terms of the characteristics of both wood and fire. Thomas Aquinas remarks that if a person answers the question of why the wood is heated by saying that God wills it, the person "answers appropriately, provided he intends to take the question back to a first cause; but not appropriately, if he means to exclude all other causes." For Thomas, there is no question that there are real causes in the natural order: "if effects are not produced by the action of created things, but only by the action of God, it is impossible for the power of any created cause to be manifested through its effects." If no created things really produced effects, then "no nature of anything would ever be known through its effect, and thus all the knowledge of natural science is taken away from us."[2]

Thomas thinks that to defend the fact that creatures are real causes, far from challenging divine omnipotence, is a powerful argument for divine omnipotence. As he says, to deny the power of creatures to be the causes of things is to detract from the perfection of creatures and, thus to detract from the perfection of God.

God is so powerful that He causes things to be and to be in certain ways. God's will transcends and constitutes the whole hierarchy of created causes, both causes which always and necessarily produce their effects and causes which at times fail to produce their effects. We can even say that God causes chance events to be chance events. The role of chance mutations at the genetic level, so important in current evolutionary theory, does not call into question God's creative act.

God is the cause of being as such — and to cause being as such is precisely what to create means. God's causation does not compete with the causation of creatures, but rather supports and grounds it. Since it is characteristic of the causes in nature precisely to be causes, God's causal determination of them is not such as to deny their proper autonomy. God causes creatures to exist in such a way that they are the real causes of their own operations. God is at work in every operation of nature, but the autonomy of nature is not an indication of some reduction in God's power or activity; rather, it is an indication of His goodness. It is not the case of partial or co-causes with each contributing a separate element to produce the effect. God and creatures can each be the complete cause of what happens, but they are causes in radically different senses – different in kind, not in degree.

In fact, God is a cause which, as one scholar aptly puts it, "differs differently" from all other causes. A robust understanding of what it means for God to create shows us that God does not only give being to things when they first begin to exist, He also causes being in them so long as they exist. He not only causes the operative powers to exist in things when these things come into being, He always causes these powers in things. Thus, if God's creative act were to cease, every operation would cease; every operation of any thing has God as its ultimate cause.

Finally, we can see that there is no need to choose between a robust view of creation as the constant exercise of divine omnipotence and the causes disclosed by the natural sciences. God's creative power is exercised throughout the entire course of cosmic history, in whatever ways that history has unfolded. No matter how random one thinks evolutionary change is, for example; no matter how much one thinks that natural selection is the master mechanism of change in the world of living things; the role of God as Creator, as continuing cause of the whole reality of all that is, is not challenged. We need to remember the fundamental point that creation is not a change, and thus there is no possibility of conflict between the explanatory domain of the natural sciences — the world of change — and that of creation.

Order, Design, and Chance in Nature

It is important to distinguish an analysis of creation from questions concerning order and design in nature, questions which are properly the subject of the empirical sciences and natural philosophy. The biologist Francisco Ayala, who has also written on the philosophical and theological implications of evolutionary biology, notes that

> . . . it was Darwin's greatest accomplishment to show that living beings and their configurations can be explained as the result of a natural process, natural selection, without any need or resort to a Creator or other external agent. . . [H]is mechanism, natural selection, excluded God as accounting for the obvious design of organisms. . . Darwin's revolutionary achievement is that he extended the Copernican revolution to the world of living things. The origin and adaptive natures of organisms could now be explained, like the phenomena of the inanimate world, as the result of natural laws manifested in natural processes.[3]

The Neo-Darwinian synthesis adds to Darwin's insight the claim that the natural process begins with chance mutations at the level of genes. Randomness and chance, as the source of whatever order and design we observe in nature, would seem to make any appeal from the evidence of biology to an author of that order unjustified. It is, however, one thing to say that the explanatory categories of evolutionary biology do not go beyond descriptions of chance and randomness as the basis for change; it is another thing to say that there is nothing more needed to account for biological change than chance and randomness.

Despite the rhetoric of some proponents of evolutionary theory and of most opponents, the natural processes at work in evolutionary change are not themselves random. As Ayala points out, "the traits that organisms acquire in their evolutionary histories are not fortuitous but are determined by their functional utility to the organisms, and they come about in small steps that accumulate over time, each step providing some reproductive advantage over the previous condition." Still, the hereditary variations with which natural selection works come about as the result of genetic mutations which are random in the sense that they occur without any relation to whether or not they are beneficial to the organisms in which they occur.

These random mutations are not events without causes. Again, in the words of Ayala, "the theory of evolution manifests chance and necessity jointly intertwined in the stuff of life; randomness and determinism interlocked in a natural process that has spurted the most complex, diverse, and beautiful entities in the universe." Furthermore, in addition to stochastic processes at the genetic level, the wider environment, physical and biological, plays an important role in the outcome of natural selection.

The reality of chance events in the evolution of living things, and whatever indeterminacy and unpredictability result, do not justify making chance an ultimate explanatory principle. Chance events occur *within* nature: within the context of a reality susceptible to rational investigation because it is intelligible, and it is this intelligibility which makes possible the laws of nature. Indeed, chance is really meaningless apart from a recognition of purpose and order. It is only because we do recognize that things act to achieve ends regularly that we recognize the failure of this to happen, that is, chance. We ought not to "absolutize" chance and randomness and make them universal principles of change, or to think that their existence in nature is a challenge to God's providential ordering of the world.

Some thinkers do use arguments which have their roots in Neo-Darwinism to deny divine providence, but only if one illegitimately raises biological arguments to the level of metaphysical and theological claims does such an error occur. Thus, the real problem lies not in the commitment of evolutionary biology to explanations in terms of randomness and contingency, but rather in unwarranted extrapolations about the absence of meaning and purpose in nature.

Providence and Transcendence

To affirm that God's purpose is achieved in a world in which there are real natural causes operating according to their own principles requires us to keep in mind that God is a transcendent cause. As we have seen, God is the universal cause of existence as such, but God is also the cause of causes. Here is the way the Catholic Church's International Theological Commission puts it:

> God's action does not displace or supplant the activity of creaturely causes, but enables them to act according to their natures and, nonetheless, to bring about the ends He intends. In freely willing to create and conserve the universe, God wills to activate and to sustain in act all those secondary causes whose activity contributes to the unfolding of the natural order which He intends to produce.[4]

Such a scenario is only intelligible if we recognize that God's causality functions at a different metaphysical level from that of any other cause. As we saw, God's causal agency does not compete with the causes in nature; nor really does God's causality "supplement" a less than adequate set of secondary causes. However much these secondary causes depend completely upon God for the fact that they exist, they exist in such a way as to be the causes of the changes which occur in nature.

The argument that the existence of randomness and chance in biological processes challenges the existence of the Creator only makes sense were one to think that for the universe to be created means that there is, finally, no place for chance events in it. Such a view mistakenly identifies a creator as a kind of super-cause *among* other causes. As we shall see, some theologians, in order to protect the autonomy of natural processes, are ready to reject divine omnipotence or to refer to God's withdrawing, so to speak, to grant an independence to nature.

At least we can say that God's providence is not threatened by evolution viewed in terms of random variations, unless, of course, one mistakenly argues that the natural sciences are the *only* source of truth about the world. An important lesson here is that we do not need to defend divine providence by rejecting evolutionary biology, but only by rejecting certain philosophical claims which deny providence.

Evolution, Intelligent Design, and Process Theology

Much of the current discussion about creation and evolution proceeds from impoverished notions of creation as well as from a failure to see the limits of scientific explanations of the world. Debates about the adequacy of various evolutionary theories often confuse categories of explanation: theological, metaphysical, natural philosophical, and scientific. One obvious error is to think that the analyses provided by the natural sciences are the only – and hence, in principle, exhaustive – rational accounts of nature, thus excluding philosophy. This error is further compounded when reason itself is viewed as the only avenue to truth, thus excluding faith.

With respect to evolution, one major confusion involves thinking that creation is essentially the production of order and design. Thus, as we have seen, some think that exclusively scientific explanations of order and design eliminate the need for a creator. On the other hand, some who contend that evolution cannot adequately account for the appearance of design in nature think that there is space available for a creator to act. In some cases this means an embrace of "special creation" according to which God directly produces each of the various species of living things; for others an "intelligent designer" is needed to supplement scientific explanations. In addition, among many contemporary thinkers, forms of process theology appear especially attractive ways to re-think creation and science, but in such a way as to abandon the traditional doctrine of creation out of nothing.

Intelligent Design

Perhaps the best known of the scientific arguments against the master narrative of evolution is the work of the biochemist, Michael Behe, who argues that there are specific life forms (e.g., the cell) and biotic subsystems which are, in his terms, "irreducibily complex," and which could not possibly be brought about by means of natural selection.

Proponents of "intelligent design" think that these "irreducible complexities" cannot be the result of random processes: ultimately, this type of design discovered by biology can only be explained by an appeal to a designer. This conclusion, they claim, is properly speaking, a scientific one. In the analysis of William Dembski, the leading theoretician of "intelligent design," natural entities which reveal what he calls "specified complexity" cannot be brought about by natural processes alone and thus must be the outcome of intelligent design. The intelligent designer is not simply the source of the form or pattern of what is designed but is also the agent cause of its production in the natural order. Irreducibly complex systems and life forms disclose "intelligent design" and lead us, ineluctably, to the existence of a designer.

Michael Behe's "irreducible complexities" are biological "singularities." And, in the hands of their defenders, their existence is strong, if not conclusive, evidence for an agent outside the regular course of nature. Most biologists respond to Behe's claims of irreducible complexity by distinguishing between our not now being able *to explain* the origin of complex structures like the cell in terms of evolutionary biology and the conclusion that *in principle* no such explanation is possible and that, therefore, we must admit the role of an intelligent designer. They might very well accept the former – the epistemological claim – but they would reject the latter – the ontological claim. As several commentators have observed, those, who argue for "irreducible complexity" and then move to claims about intelligent design, represent a contemporary version of what has been called the "god of the gaps." This is the view that the natural order *itself* and the changes in it require an appeal to a divine agent operating within the world as a *supplement to* other agents and causes in the world.

The "god" in the "god of the gaps" is more powerful than any other agent in nature, but such a god is not the God of orthodox Christianity, Islam, and Judaism. The "god of the gaps" or the intelligent designer of Behe's analysis becomes a cause *within* the world and is not the Creator. Regardless of what one might think of the arguments of "intelligent design," they are not really about creation.

Process Theology and the Denial of Creation Out of Nothing

There are some scholars who think that, in the light of modern science, radical revisions (rather than outright rejections) are required in what it means for God to create. God can no longer be considered either omnipotent or immutable; rather, He evolves as the universe evolves. Only such a less than all-powerful God could be consistent, so it is thought, with a world rich with its own powers of change and generation. To this end, the very doctrine of creation out of nothing must be rejected since it has its basis in an outmoded conception of God.

In this tradition, John Haught of Georgetown University, in a highly influential book, *God After Darwin: A Theology of Evolution* (2000), justified his subject with a sweeping, initial claim: "Any thoughts we may have about God after the life and work of Charles Darwin (1809-1882) can hardly remain the same as before. Evolutionary science has changed our understanding of the world dramatically, and so any sense we may have of a God who creates and cares for this world must take into account what Darwin and his followers have told us about it." For process theologians, the source of conflict between science and religion, from the side of religion, is the very doctrine of creation *ex nihilo*, since, according to them, this doctrine involves a commitment to divine omnipotence which is incompatible with the discovery of any kind of causality or power inherent in nature. Such theologians find in the thought of Alfred North Whitehead (1861-1947) the key to a proper *rapprochement* between science and theology.

Although evolutionary science has significantly changed our view of the world and of ourselves, I am not persuaded that our thoughts about God need to undergo a radical revision. Of course, it depends on the particular thoughts about God to which one is referring. "As long as we think of God," Haught writes, "only in terms of 'order' or 'design,' the 'atheism' of many evolutionists will seem appropriate." Rather than accept the conclusions of the "new atheism," Haught and others urge a "new theism" consistent with the evolving universe disclosed by contemporary science.

As I have suggested, this "new theism" follows Whitehead's emphasis on nature as a process of becoming and his explicit rejection of creation *ex nihilo*. Whitehead thinks that the kind of "extreme voluntarism" which sees God "as the one supreme reality, omnipotently disposing a wholly derivative world" is absolutely incompatible with a true science of nature, since to claim that something can come from nothing violates the tenets of science. Creation, at least as traditionally understood, must be rejected if we are to honor what science tells us about the world. It seems to me, however, that a process-theological view of God who changes as the world changes, fails to do justice either to God or to creation. As we have seen, the doctrine of creation out of nothing is fully compatible with the integrity of the natural order, with its rich array of dynamic causes. We do not need to abandon creation out of nothing in order to honor the achievements of science.

Kenosis

Closely associated with process theology is what is sometimes referred to as a kenotic theology of creation. This is the view that, given the insights of chaos theory, complexity theory, and dynamic self-organization in nature, we need to see God as withdrawing, so to speak, in order to allow new order and new life "to unfold with spontaneity, freedom, and creativity." John Haught speaks of a "metaphysics of humility" as the basis of divine action. The position often affirmed is that somehow God must be limited or self-limited or "humble" in order for nature to be marked by the novelty and surprise which evolutionary biology discovers in the world. Novelty and surprise are incompatible with "programmed blueprints" so often associated with the view of God as designer. In a broader sense, such theologians think that traditional conceptions of God as omnipotent, omniscient, and beyond time, based as they are on a "metaphysics of being," need to be replaced as a result of a new understanding of reality, a "metaphysics of becoming."

Keeping with his general theme that evolutionary biology offers a gift to theology, Haught thinks that modern science shows us that we live in a universe that in important ways is not yet fully created. There is no perfect created order from which the physical suffering in the world must be seen as a defect. If the world is developing, is in a sense unfinished, then "we cannot justifiably expect it yet to be perfect." The world "*inevitably* has a dark side." Haught insists that "the only kind of universe" a loving God could create is an evolving universe.

Here we see the frequent view that a God of love must be a self-limiting God in order to allow creatures to have an appropriate autonomy. As our discussion of creation in the traditional sense has shown, one need not choose between a self-limiting God of love with a relative autonomy for nature, on the one hand, and an immutable, omnipotent God with a completed, static natural order, on the other. With a proper understanding of divine agency and divine transcendence, there is no reason for God to limit His power and presence in order to provide space in which to create or space in which creatures can exercise their own agency (including the agency of evolutionary change that results in real novelty in nature).

We can accept an important feature of Haught's analysis without rejecting, as he does, a traditional view of God as Creator. The traditional sense of creation is perfectly compatible with an evolving universe. The "creation" which is, according to Haught, not yet finished is the world of changing things, ever open to new and unexpected varieties of things. Such a changing world, with all its novelty, is being created by God; the traditional sense of creation does not limit it to some once-and-for-all distant event, nor does it require that the world be a static, "programmed blueprint."

Denying divine omnipotence, immutability, and the like, is surely more appealing than the crude atheism of Richard Dawkins, Daniel Dennett, Christopher Hitchens, and others, but, I think, it too suffers from a failure to take seriously the insights of Thomas Aquinas and others who have provided us with the traditional understanding of creation. I think that Haught, and process theologians in general, underestimate the resources of traditional philosophy and theology to respond to the evidence of modern biology and cosmology.

It seems to me that the various theological attempts to re-configure our understanding of God and of creation in the context of contemporary science begin with an inadequate understanding of the richness of the traditional doctrines of God and creation. Although these theologies reject atheism as a necessary conclusion of the developments of science, they tend to share a common commitment to the view that science has made the traditional notion of God as Creator either irrelevant or false.

Evil and Evolution's Gift to Theology: A Postscript

The pain and suffering disclosed in the world of evolutionary change, a world beset by struggles for existence, or in the famous words, "nature, red in tooth and claw," have served some as added evidence for the impossibility of affirming the existence of an all-powerful and all-good God. Several years ago, David Hull, philosopher of biology, asked rhetorically: "What kind of God can one infer from the sort of phenomena epitomized by the species on Darwin's Galapagos Islands? The evolutionary process is rife with happenstance, contingency, incredible waste, death, pain and horror. . . .The God of the Galapagos is careless, wasteful, indifferent, and almost diabolical. He is certainly not the sort of God to whom anyone would be inclined to pray." Although evidence from biology may bring the problem of evil in nature to our attention with a particular clarity, if not poignancy, it is not a really new argument against creation and divine providence.

Some theologians have argued that the physical evil, rampant in a world described by evolution, is a gift to theology since we now have a purely natural explanation for the pain and suffering which is all around us. We have seen Haught argue that creation is not yet completed, not yet perfected, and thus we should expect a "dark side" to reality. God can no longer be held responsible for physical evil. Of course, the God who is no longer responsible is the God who allows nature to take its own course; such a God, however, is no longer the omnipotent Creator of all that is.

It does not seem to me that contemporary science provides any new insights for the ancient discussion of what has been called "the problem of evil" - on either side of the issue.

Conclusion: Hawking's Universe

When Stephen Hawking was in New York in June 2010 to participate in a celebration of contemporary science, he remarked to a reporter that he hoped that eventually the universe would provide an answer to a question which continues to intrigue him: why does the universe exist? Indeed, he phrased the question in a traditional form: why is there something rather than nothing? These are questions raised in his recent book, *The Grand Design* (2010), co-authored with fellow physicist Leonard Mlodinow. The cover of the book announces as a kind of subtitle: "The World's Most Famous Scientist Addresses the Meaning of the Universe." Speculations about "the meaning of the universe" can also be found in Hawking's earlier books, *A Brief History of Time* (1988) and *The Universe in a Nutshell* (2001). Where Hawking might look for such meaning may be indicated by his famous remark that the universe is "completely self-contained and not affected by anything outside itself".

Referring to Hawking's new book can serve as a fitting reminder of what I have discussed in many sections of this book. In *The Grand Design*, Hawking claims: "Spontaneous creation is the reason there is something rather than nothing, why the Universe exists, why we exist. It is not necessary to invoke God . . . to set the Universe going." Citing a version of contemporary string theory, known as "M-theory," Hawking tells us that the "creation" of a great many universes out of nothing "does not require the intervention of some supernatural being or god." Rather, these multiple universes "arise naturally from physical law." Ultimate questions about the nature of existence which have intrigued philosophers for millennia are, so he claims, now the province of science, and "philosophy is dead." Hawking telling us that it is not necessary "to invoke God . . .to set the Universe going." But creation does not mean "to set the Universe going" – as though some change occurred at a putative beginning. As we have seen, a proper understanding of creation reminds us that to deny some initial change, as Hawking does, is not to deny creation.

To explain order and design in terms of processes within nature does not eliminate the need for a Creator, a Creator who is responsible for the existence of nature and everything in it. Hawking thinks that modern arguments about design, especially those which refer to the remarkable coincidence of the initial conditions of the universe (the so-called strong anthropic principle), do not lead us to the existence of a Grand Designer. Rather, "the fine-tunings in the laws of nature can be explained by the existence of multiple universes." We just happen to live in that universe (among perhaps an infinite number of other universes) which has the right environment for us. Indeed, he notes, "just as Darwin . . . explained how the apparently miraculous design of living forms could appear without intervention by a supreme being, the multiverse concept can explain the fine-tuning of physical law without the need for a benevolent creator who made the universe for our benefit." The Grand Designer rejected by Hawking is not the Creator, at least not the Creator which traditional philosophy and theology affirms.

In *The Grand Design*, Hawking, granting a near omnicompetence to the natural sciences, writes: "Because there is a law such as gravity, the Universe can and will create itself from nothing."[5] But there would be no gravity, indeed there would be nothing at all, were God not to be creating all that is as it is.

Throughout this book I have sought to show that questions concerning the very existence of things, including the universe as a whole, are not proper subjects for the natural sciences. The latter concern changes in and among things, not why there is something rather than nothing. Hawking's question as to why the universe exists is not a cosmological question; it is a metaphysical and a theological question, and the answer is not to be found in the natural sciences but in metaphysics and theology. Hawking and many other cosmologists and commentators on cosmology tend to have a notion of creation and of a Creator which pales in significance to the traditional sense of these terms, which I have sought to make clear in this book.

Much of Hawking's analysis hinges on his concern about the beginning of the universe and what can and cannot be said about it – indeed, whether or not the very notion of a beginning is intelligible. But the fundamental sense of creation, that sense disclosed in metaphysics, prescinds from questions about beginnings; instead it concerns origins, the complete dependence of all that is on God as cause. Thus, as we saw Thomas Aquinas conclude, there is no contradiction in the idea of a universe, eternal and created. Furthermore, too often a creator is viewed as an agent (albeit a very powerful one) cause of change; thus, to deny an initial change is thought to mean a denial of creation. But, creation is not a change at all.

The failure to recognize that creation is not a change, coupled with the failure to distinguish creation from the production of order and design, is evident in discourse about the relationship between evolution and creation. This failure leads not only to the denial of creation (for example, among the "new atheists") but to radical reconfigurations of God as Creator. We have seen the latter in process theology which denies that God is omnipotent and immutable and rejects the idea of creation out of nothing. One popular author, illustrative of some contemporary trends in this regard, is Robert Wright.

Reminiscent of early modern deism, Wright thinks that any reconciliation between evolution and theology requires that "modern theology . . . bite the bullet and accept the fact that God did his work remotely – that his role in the creative process ended when he unleashed the algorithm of natural selection (whether by dropping it into the primordial ooze or writing its eventual emergence into the initial conditions of the universe or whatever)." Admitting that his "theo-biological scenario," according to which God initiated natural selection with "some confidence that it would lead to a morally rich and reflective species," is only speculative, Wright concludes that "these speculations are compatible with the standard scientific theory of human creation." Furthermore, if believers would accept them, "it would end any conflict between religion and the teaching of evolutionary biology." Were theology to follow this path it would, according to Wright, author of *The Evolution of God* (2009), do what it has done before: "evolve – adapt its conception of God to advancing knowledge and to sheer logic."

The complete dependence of all that is on God does not challenge an appropriate autonomy of natural causation; God is not a competing cause in a world of other causes. In fact, God's causality is such that he causes creatures to be the kind of causal agents which they are. In an important sense, there would be no autonomy to the natural order were God not causing it to be so: there would be no cosmological or evolutionary processes at all were God not creating them to be and to be what they are. Traditional conceptions of God as Creator certainly need not be abandoned in order to embrace an evolving universe.

The natural sciences, philosophy, and theology discover complementary, not competing, truths about nature, human nature, and God. Not only is there no contradiction between creation and the natural sciences, without creation there would be no science at all.

Further Reading

Benedict Ashley, *The Way Toward Wisdom*.

Steven E. Baldner and William E. Carroll, *Aquinas on Creation*.

William E. Carroll, "Creation and the Foundations of Evolution," *Angelicum* 87 (2010), 45-60.

William E. Carroll, "At the Mercy of Chance? Evolution and the Catholic Tradition," *Revue des Questions Scientifiques* 177:2 (2006), 179-204.

William E. Carroll, "Big Bang Cosmology, Quantum Tunneling from Nothing, and Creation," *Laval théologique et philosophique*, 44, 1 (1988) 59-75.

William Lane Craig and Quentin Smith, *Theism, Atheism, and Big Bang Cosmology*.

Denis Edwards, *How God Acts, Creation, Redemption, and Special Divine Action*.

Francisco José Soler Gil (ed.), *Dios y las cosmologías modernas*.

John F. Haught, *Making Sense of Evolution. Darwin, God, and the Drama of Life*.

Jean-Michel Maldamé, *Création et Providence: Bible, science, et philosophie*.

Ernan McMullin (ed.), *Evolution and Creation*.

Don O'Leary, *Roman Catholicism and Modern Science*.

Josef Cardinal Ratzinger, *'In the Beginning . . .' A Catholic Understanding of the Story of Creation and the Fall*.

Christoph Cardinal Schönborn, *Chance or Purpose? Creation, Evolution, and a Rational Faith*.

Józef Życiński, *God and Evolution*.

Endnotes

[1] The argument involves a recognition that the difference between what things are (their essences) and that they are (their existence) must ultimately be resolved in a reality (God) in whom essence and existence are identical. Thus, what it means to be God is to be, and God is the uncaused cause of all beings. One need not accept the validity of Thomas' claim to demonstrate that the universe is created in order to understand his distinction between creation and science and that "to create" is not to produce a change.

[2] *Summa contra Gentiles* III, cc. 64 and 69.

[3] Francisco J. Ayala, "Design without Designer: Darwin's Greatest Discovery," in *Debating Design: From Darwin to DNA*, edited by William A. Dembski and Michael Ruse (2004), 55-80.

[4] *Communion and Strewardship* (2004), paragraph 68.

[5] "The ultimate theory must be consistent and must predict finite results for quantities that we can measure. We've seen that there must be a law such as gravity, and for a theory of gravity to predict finite quantities, the theory must have what is called supersymmetry between the forces of nature and the matter on which they act. M-theory is the most general supersymmetric theory of gravity. For these reasons M-theory is the only complete theory of the Universe. If it is finite – and this is yet to be proved – it will be a model of a Universe that creates itself." (Hawking, *The Grand Design*.)

Galileo - Science & Faith

The Galileo controversy has become a paragon of faith's supposed hostility towards science. Galileo believed that the earth rotated around the sun but did not have sufficient evidence to prove it. The Inquisition believed that unless such evidence existed the sun should continue to be considered to rotate around the earth. This booklet explains the facts of the Galileo case and traces the subsequent development of the myth that the Catholic Church has always been the enemy of science. This history proves that even in the Galileo case the Church remained true to its belief that faith and reason belong together.

ISBN: 978 1 86082 546 0

CTS Code: H509

Darwin & Evolution

Darwin's theories led him from faith to agnosticism, and ever since their publication his ideas have been the battleground between faith and science, creation and evolution. This booklet considers whether evolution and faith really are incompatible, what the Catholic Church teaches regarding creation and whether science really can answer humanity's greatest question: why am I here?

Joseph Bolin is a seminarian of the Archdiocese of Vienna and Assistant Professor of Theology at the International Theological Institute in Trumau, Austria.

ISBN: 978 1 86082 610 8

CTS Code: Ex31